a Year of Enchantment

My Baby Record Book

Lisa Jane

Cedco Publishing
San Rafael, California

ISBN: 0-7683-2376-2

Published in 2001 by Cedco Publishing Company
100 Pelican Way, San Rafael California 94901
For a free catalog of other Cedco® products,
please write to the address above, or visit our Web site.
www.cedco.com

Book design by Sascha Hutchings
Cover design by Teena Gores

Printed in Hong Kong

3 5 7 9 10 8 6 4 2

This book belongs to

_____

a truly enchanting baby

Table of Contents

$\mathcal{M}$y $\mathcal{M}$ommy

$\mathcal{M}$y Mommy's name _____

$\mathcal{H}$er birthday is _____

$\mathcal{S}$he was born in _____

$\mathcal{S}$he grew up in _____

Picture

of my

Mommy

$\mathcal{S}$he likes to _____

_____

_____

_____

_____

$\mathcal{M}$y $\mathcal{D}$addy

$\mathcal{M}$y Daddy's name _____

$\mathcal{H}$is birthday is _____

$\mathcal{H}$e was born in _____

$\mathcal{H}$e grew up in _____

$\mathcal{H}$e likes to _____

_____

_____

_____

_____

Picture
of my
Daddy

Finding Out

*H*ow they found out they were having me _____
_____
_____

*M*ommy's reaction _____
_____
_____

*D*addy's reaction _____
_____
_____

*M*y due date _____

*W*ho they told first _____

*A*dvice and excitement _____
_____
_____
_____
_____
_____

Mommy & I Are Growing!

*S*he felt _____

*F*oods Mommy craved _____
_____ *&* avoided _____
_____

*B*ooks she read _____
_____

*F*unny things that happened while Mommy was pregnant _____
_____
_____

*M*ommy's doctor's name _____

Picture of my Mommy

(with me inside!)

5

Getting Ready

*M*ommy and Daddy got their house ready by _____
_____
_____
_____
_____

*S*hopping trips_____
_____
_____
_____

*T*hings they bought _____
_____
_____
_____
_____

*T*hings they were given_____
_____
_____
_____
_____
_____
_____

$\mathcal{C}$hildbirth classes ——————————————————————

——

——

$\mathcal{S}$pecial health and beauty routines ——————————————

——

——

$\mathcal{W}$hat they brought to the hospital ——————————————

——

——

——

——

$\mathcal{O}$ther ways they got ready for me ——————————————

——

——

——

——

——

——

$\mathcal{S}$howers $\mathcal{\&}$ $\mathcal{P}$arties

$\mathcal{E}$vent _____

$\mathcal{D}$ate _____

$\mathcal{H}$ost _____

$\mathcal{G}$ames, food, and other fun things _____

_____

_____

$\mathcal{G}$uests and gifts _____

_____

_____

_____

_____

_____

_____

_____

_____

_____

_____

Photos

&

invitations

Happy Birthday!

I was born on _____
          day   date   time

I weighed _____ & measured _____

My eye color _____ My hair color _____

Picture of me

Special memories of my birth _____
_____
_____
_____
_____

*M*ommy's first thoughts and words

_____
_____
_____
_____
_____
_____
_____
_____
_____

*D*addy's first thoughts and words _____

_____
_____
_____
_____
_____
_____
_____
_____
_____
_____

*O*ther people who were there _____

_____
_____
_____
_____
_____
_____
_____
_____
_____
_____

My full name

_____

What my names mean _____

_____

_____

_____

_____

How my name was chosen _____

_____

_____

_____

_____

_____

Other names considered _____

_____

_____

_____

_____

_____

_____

Birth certificate,
birth announcement &
newspaper clippings

Welcome to the World!

When I was born

The country's leaders were _____
_____

The national news events were _____
_____
_____
_____

Local leaders and events were _____
_____
_____
_____

The economy was _____

_____

_____

_____

_____

_____

People were thinking about _____
_____
_____
_____
_____
_____

*H*it movies were _____
_____
_____

*M*ommy's and Daddy's favorite TV shows were _____
_____
_____

*B*est-selling books were _____
_____
_____

*P*opular songs were _____
_____
_____

*T*he latest high-tech gadgets were _____
_____
_____

*T*he latest fashion trends and hot designers were _____
_____
_____

*O*ur monthly house payment or rent was _____

A gallon of gas cost _____

A movie ticket cost _____

A diaper cost _____

15

My First Day Home!

Photo

Date _____

Where we lived _____

Who was there _____

_____

_____

What we did _____

_____

_____

16

Homecoming

photos

& photos of

my house

Greetings, Gifts & Visitors

Handprints & Footprints

At Birth

Handprints & Footprints

At One Year

Ceremonies & Celebrations

$\mathcal{E}$vent _____

$\mathcal{D}$ate _____

$\mathcal{W}$hat we did _____
_____
_____
_____

$\mathcal{W}$ho was there _____
_____
_____
_____

$\mathcal{S}$pecial memories _____
_____
_____
_____
_____
_____
_____
_____
_____

Photos,

invitations &

mementos

My Family

*B*rothers and sisters _____
_____
_____

*G*randmothers and grandfathers _____
_____

*G*reat-grandmothers and great-grandfathers _____
_____

*A*unts and uncles _____
_____
_____

*C*ousins _____
_____
_____
_____
_____
_____
_____

*O*ther people in my family _____
_____
_____
_____
_____
_____
_____

Photos
of my
family

Nighty Night!

Photos

Mommy and Daddy know it's time for bed when I _____

_____

At night I sleep in _____

My favorite places to sleep are _____

_____

Before I go to bed I _____

_____

$\mathcal{I}$ wake up by _____

$\mathcal{M}$y favorite pajamas and blankets are

_____

_____

_____

_____

_____

_____

Photos

So Many Firsts!

The first time I...

Slept through the night _____

Smiled _____

Had a bath in the tub _____

Laughed _____

Discovered hands _____

& feet _____

Rolled from back to front _____

& front to back _____

*A*te solid food ——————————————————————

*C*rawled ——————————————————————

*S*tood ——————————————————————

*W*alked——————————————————————

*C*ut a tooth ——————————————————————

*W*aved "Bye-bye" ——————————————————————

*G*ot a haircut ——————————————————————

*S*poke a word ——————————————————————

Tape a
lock of hair
here

My Favorite Things

People _____
_____
_____
_____
_____
_____

Toys _____
_____
_____

Songs _____
_____
_____
_____
_____

Colors _____
_____

Books _____
_____
_____
_____
_____
_____
_____

$\mathcal{F}$ood _____

_____

_____

_____

$\mathcal{TV}$ shows or videos _____

_____

_____

_____

$\mathcal{P}$laces in my house _____

_____

_____

$\mathcal{C}$lothes _____

_____

_____

$\mathcal{O}$ther favorites _____

_____

_____

_____

_____

_____

_____

_____

_____

_____

_____

_____

Healthy & Growing!

I went to the doctor...

Date _____ Reason _____

Treatments _____

How I reacted _____

_____

Date _____ Reason _____

Treatments _____

How I reacted _____

_____

Date _____ Reason _____

Treatments _____

How I reacted _____

_____

Date _____ Reason _____

Treatments _____

How I reacted _____

_____

$\mathcal{D}$ate $\mathcal{A}$ge $\mathcal{I}$ weighed $\mathcal{I}$ measured

$\mathcal{D}$ate $\mathcal{A}$ge $\mathcal{I}$ weighed $\mathcal{I}$ measured

$\mathcal{D}$ate $\mathcal{A}$ge $\mathcal{I}$ weighed $\mathcal{I}$ measured

$\mathcal{D}$ate $\mathcal{A}$ge $\mathcal{I}$ weighed $\mathcal{I}$ measured

$\mathcal{D}$ate $\mathcal{A}$ge $\mathcal{I}$ weighed $\mathcal{I}$ measured

$\mathcal{D}$ate $\mathcal{A}$ge $\mathcal{I}$ weighed $\mathcal{I}$ measured

$\mathcal{D}$ate $\mathcal{A}$ge $\mathcal{I}$ weighed $\mathcal{I}$ measured

$\mathcal{D}$ate $\mathcal{A}$ge $\mathcal{I}$ weighed $\mathcal{I}$ measured

Travel & Outings

Photo

*P*laces I go in my neighborhood _____

_____

*O*n my first vacation I went _____

_____

_____

*M*y first plane ride was _____

_____

_____

*T*he first time I went on a train

_____

_____

34

Photos

Other places I like to visit _____
_____
_____
_____
_____
_____
_____
_____

Spring
Holidays

*H*olidays I celebrated _____
_____

*W*hat I did _____
_____
_____
_____

*N*ew foods I ate _____
_____
_____
_____

Photo

Photos

Photos

*H*olidays I celebrated _____

_____

*W*hat I did _____

_____

_____

_____

_____

*N*ew foods I ate _____

_____

_____

_____

Summer

Holidays

Photo

Autumn Holidays

Photos

Photos

*H*olidays I celebrated ——————————————————————

————————————————————————————————

*W*hat I did ——————————————————————————

————————————————————————————————

————————————————————————————————

————————————————————————————————

————————————————————————————————

————————————————————————————————

*N*ew foods I ate ——————————————————————

————————————————————————————————

————————————————————————————————

————————————————————————————————

Winter Holidays

Photo

*H*olidays I celebrated _____
_____

*W*hat I did _____
_____
_____
_____
_____

*N*ew foods I ate _____
_____
_____
_____

Photos

My First Month

Photos

Photos

$\mathcal{N}$ew things I do _____

_____

_____

$\mathcal{M}$ommy and Daddy's thoughts and reflections _____

_____

_____

_____

_____

_____

_____

_____

My Second Month

Photo

New things I do _____

_____

Mommy and Daddy's thoughts
and reflections _____
_____
_____
_____
_____
_____
_____
_____
_____
_____

Photos

My Third Month

Photos

Photos

*N*ew things I do _____
_____
_____

*M*ommy and Daddy's thoughts and reflections _____
_____
_____
_____
_____
_____
_____
_____

My Fourth Month

Photos

*N*ew things I do _____
_____
_____

*M*ommy and Daddy's thoughts and reflections _____
_____
_____
_____
_____
_____
_____
_____

Photos

My Fifth Month

Photos

Photos

New things I do _____

_____

_____

Mommy and Daddy's thoughts and reflections _____

_____

_____

_____

_____

_____

_____

_____

My Sixth Month

Photos

New things I do _____

_____

Mommy and Daddy's thoughts and reflections_____

_____

_____

_____

_____

_____

_____

_____

_____

Photos

My Seventh Month

Photos

Photos

*N*ew things I do _____
_____
_____

*M*ommy and Daddy's thoughts and reflections _____
_____
_____
_____
_____
_____
_____
_____

My
Eighth
Month

Photos

Photos

$\mathcal{N}$ew things I do _____
_____
_____

$\mathcal{M}$ommy and Daddy's thoughts and reflections _____
_____
_____
_____
_____
_____
_____
_____

My Ninth Month

Photo

*N*ew things I do _____
_____

*M*ommy and Daddy's thoughts and reflections_____
_____
_____
_____
_____
_____
_____
_____

Photos

My Tenth Month

Photos

Photos

*N*ew things I do _____

_____

*M*ommy and Daddy's thoughts and reflections _____

_____

_____

_____

_____

_____

_____

_____

My
Eleventh
Month

Photos

New things I do _____

_____

Mommy and Daddy's thoughts and reflections_____

_____

_____

_____

_____

_____

_____

Photos

My First Birthday!

*H*ow we celebrated _____
_____
_____
_____
_____

*W*ho was there _____
_____
_____

*G*ifts and greetings _____
_____
_____
_____
_____
_____

*H*ow I enjoyed the day _____
_____
_____
_____
_____
_____
_____
_____
_____
_____

Invitations,
cards &
photos

Photos

Photos

A Letter from Mommy

A Letter from Daddy

When I look into the eyes of a baby, I cannot help but see the ethereal magic and innocence of new life, and dream of their future full of laughter, love and wonderment. My own three boys bring me joy and fill my heart with love everyday. To all the parents and parents-to-be that record their baby's lives in this book: I hope it reminds you through all the years of your life of this very special time when, to your baby, all the world is new and beautiful and magical. Cherish these days, for they are so short. May God bless you and your sweet angel baby.

Lisa Jane

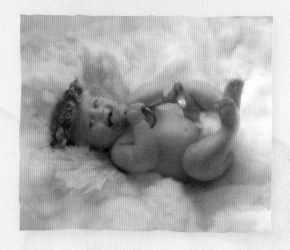

About

Lisa Jane

$\mathscr{L}$isa Jane creates her magical images at Eden Studio, her own enchanted garden complete with lily pond, sweeping veranda, and gazebo, located on three wooded acres in the heart of Houston, Texas. Lisa Jane grew up in Portland, Texas, and started taking pictures in high school. She has worked as a professional photographer ever since, graduating from Sam Houston State University, in Huntsville, with a Bachelor of Arts degree in photography and a minor in art. (The university has since given her an Honorary Professor of Photography degree as well.) When she graduated, her father offered her the choice between a Hassleblad camera and a safari to Africa as a graduation present. She took the camera and never looked back. For over twenty years Lisa Jane's creative talent, impressive technical skills, and distinctive style have earned her virtually every major degree and honor in photography. Her new art form, combining painted art, photography, and digital art, uniquely captures the beauty and wonder of childhood.